HOPSCOTCH
FAIRY TALES

Little Red
Riding Hood

MA

First published in 2008 by
Franklin Watts
338 Euston Road
London
NW1 3BH

Franklin Watts Australia
Level 17/207 Kent Street
Sydney
NSW 2000

A CIP catalogue record for this book is available
from the British Library.

ISBN 978 0 7496 7901 9 (hbk)
ISBN 978 0 7496 7907 1 (pbk)

Series Editor: Melanie Palmer
Series Advisor: Dr Barrie Wade
Series Designer: Peter Scoulding

Printed in China

Franklin Watts is a division of
Hachette Children's Books,
an Hachette Livre UK company.

HOPSCOTCH
FAIRY TALES

Little Red Riding Hood

by Anne Walter and Marjorie Dumortier

W
FRANKLIN WATTS
LONDON•SYDNEY

Long ago, a girl called
Little Red Riding Hood
lived in a village by a wood.

One day, her mother said, "Little Red Riding Hood, your granny is poorly. Please take her this basket to cheer her up."

"But remember – don't talk to any strangers on the way," she added.

Little Red Riding Hood set off
straight away. She had not gone far
when she felt a tap on her shoulder.

It was the big bad wolf!
"What a tasty snack she will
make," he thought.

"Are you lost, little girl?"
asked the wolf, smiling.
"No," said Little Red Riding Hood.
"I'm going to visit my granny.
She lives by the stream."

"Really!" grinned the wolf,
licking his lips.

11

Litte Red Riding Hood picked up
the basket and hurried on her way.

The wolf also rushed to Granny's
house. "Granny lunch with little
girl pudding – delicious!" he thought.

13

The wolf knocked on Granny's door.

"Come in, dear," called Granny.

14

The wolf let himself in and
swallowed Granny whole!

Then the wolf quickly put on
a nightgown and frilly cap,
and got into granny's bed.

16

Soon, Little Red Riding Hood arrived.

"Granny, it's Little Red Riding Hood."

"Come in dear!" called the wolf in
his squeakiest voice.

When Little Red Riding Hood
went inside, she could hardly
recognise Granny.

"Oh Granny, you sound terrible!"
said Little Red Riding Hood.
"I have a cold, dear," said the wolf.

"Granny, what big ears you have!"
said Little Red Riding Hood.

"All the better to hear you with,"
replied the wolf.

"Granny, what big eyes you have!"
said Little Red Riding Hood.
"All the better to see you with,"
replied the wolf.

23

"Granny, what big teeth you have!"
said Little Red Riding Hood.

"All the better to EAT you with!"
roared the wolf and he leapt out
of the bed.

Little Red Riding Hood ran as fast as she could out of Granny's house. "Help! Help!" she screamed.

The wolf tried to run after her,
but he tripped over the nightgown.

Help!

Luckily, a woodcutter was nearby.
He grabbed the wolf and made
him cough up Granny.

Then the woodcutter chased the
wolf far away, deep into the wood.

Little Red Riding Hood and Granny
sat down to share the tasty cake
from Mother's basket.

"I promise never talk to strangers again," said Little Red Riding Hood.

Hopscotch has been specially designed to fit the requirements of the Literacy Framework. It offers real books by top authors and illustrators for children developing their reading skills. There are 55 Hopscotch stories to choose from:

Marvin, the Blue Pig
ISBN 978 0 7496 4619 6

Plip and Plop
ISBN 978 0 7496 4620 2

The Queen's Dragon
ISBN 978 0 7496 4618 9

Flora McQuack
ISBN 978 0 7496 4621 9

Willie the Whale
ISBN 978 0 7496 4623 3

Naughty Nancy
ISBN 978 0 7496 4622 6

Run!
ISBN 978 0 7496 4705 6

The Playground Snake
ISBN 978 0 7496 4706 3

"Sausages!"
ISBN 978 0 7496 4707 0

Bear in Town
ISBN 978 0 7496 5875 5

Pippin's Big Jump
ISBN 978 0 7496 4710 0

Whose Birthday Is It?
ISBN 978 0 7496 4709 4

The Princess and the Frog
ISBN 978 0 7496 5129 9

Flynn Flies High
ISBN 978 0 7496 5130 5

Clever Cat
ISBN 978 0 7496 5131 2

Moo!
ISBN 978 0 7496 5332 3

Izzie's Idea
ISBN 978 0 7496 5334 7

Roly-poly Rice Ball
ISBN 978 0 7496 5333 0

I Can't Stand It!
ISBN 978 0 7496 5765 9

Cockerel's Big Egg
ISBN 978 0 7496 5767 3

How to Teach a Dragon Manners
ISBN 978 0 7496 5873 1

The Truth about those Billy Goats
ISBN 978 0 7496 5766 6

Marlowe's Mum and the Tree House
ISBN 978 0 7496 5874 8

The Truth about Hansel and Gretel
ISBN 978 0 7496 4708 7

The Best Den Ever
ISBN 978 0 7496 5876 2

ADVENTURE STORIES

Aladdin and the Lamp
ISBN 978 0 7496 6692 7

Blackbeard the Pirate
ISBN 978 0 7496 6690 3

George and the Dragon
ISBN 978 0 7496 6691 0

Jack the Giant-Killer
ISBN 978 0 7496 6693 4

TALES OF KING ARTHUR

1. The Sword in the Stone
ISBN 978 0 7496 6694 1

2. Arthur the King
ISBN 978 0 7496 6695 8

3. The Round Table
ISBN 978 0 7496 6697 2

4. Sir Lancelot and the Ice Castle
ISBN 978 0 7496 6698 9

TALES OF ROBIN HOOD

Robin and the Knight
ISBN 978 0 7496 6699 6

Robin and the Monk
ISBN 978 0 7496 6700 9

Robin and the Silver Arrow
ISBN 978 0 7496 6703 0

Robin and the Friar
ISBN 978 0 7496 6702 3

FAIRY TALES

The Emperor's New Clothes
ISBN 978 0 7496 7421 2

Cinderella
ISBN 978 0 7496 7417 5

Snow White
ISBN 978 0 7496 7418 2

Jack and the Beanstalk
ISBN 978 0 7496 7422 9

The Three Billy Goats Gruff
ISBN 978 0 7496 7420 5

The Pied Piper of Hamelin
ISBN 978 0 7496 7419 9

Goldilocks and the Three Bears
ISBN 978 0 7496 7897 5 *
ISBN 978 0 7496 7903 3

Hansel and Gretel
ISBN 978 0 7496 7898 2 *
ISBN 978 0 7496 7904 0

The Three Little Pigs
ISBN 978 0 7496 7899 9 *
ISBN 978 0 7496 7905 7

Rapunzel
ISBN 978 0 7496 7900 2 *
ISBN 978 0 7496 7906 4

Little Red Riding Hood
ISBN 978 0 7496 7901 9 *
ISBN 978 0 7496 7907 1

Rumpelstiltskin
ISBN 978 0 7496 7902 6*
ISBN 978 0 7496 7908 8

HISTORIES

Toby and the Great Fire of London
ISBN 978 0 7496 7410 6

Pocahontas the Peacemaker
ISBN 978 0 7496 7411 3

Grandma's Seaside Bloomers
ISBN 978 0 7496 7412 0

Hoorah for Mary Seacole
ISBN 978 0 7496 7413 7

Remember the 5th of November
ISBN 978 0 7496 7414 4

Tutankhamun and the Golden Chariot
ISBN 978 0 7496 7415 1

* **hardback**